The front cover

Look at the front cover.

What is the story about?

Which elephant do you think is Mantu?

How do Mantu and his mother feel?

The back cover

Let's read the blurb together.

What sort of trouble might there be around the next bend in the river?

The title page

How do you think Mantu feels in this picture? (*sad, disappointed*)

Who is the author? (*Malachy Doyle*). Who is the illustrator? (*Giuliano Ferri*)

Lesson 1 (Chapter 1)

READ

Read pages 2 to 5

Purpose: To find out what the author tells us about the place where Mantu was born.

PAUSE

Pause at page 5

What does the text tell us about the African plains?

What can you tell about Mantu and his mother from the illustration on pages 2 and 3?

Why do you think all the elephants came to stroke Mantu?

What words in the text describe the African plains where Mantu was born? (*wide open sky, hot, dusty land*)

Discuss the phrase 'wise, old elephant'. Why do the words 'old' and 'wise' go together? (*age brings experience*)

Chapter 1

Mantu was born under the wide open sky.
His mother stroked him with her trunk.
Mantu was her first baby.
   The other elephants all came to stroke Mantu.
Then his mother helped him onto his legs,
and fed him.

Mantu grew fast. The sun was strong and
the land grew dry. Every day, the elephants
marched across the hot, dusty land. Every
day, they had to march further and further
to find food and water. Mantu held onto his
mother's tail with his trunk.

One day the sun was **very** strong.
   "I'm so thirsty!" Mantu cried.
   "Don't worry," said his mother. "We'll find water.
Kim, the wise old elephant, knows where to go."

READ

Read pages 6 to 7

Purpose: To search for two types of information:
to find out about Mantu
to find any references to Kim's age and wisdom.

PAUSE

Pause at page 7

How thirsty was Mantu? Why could he not jump in the river?

Why did Kim go in the water first? Why is Kim the leader of the elephants?

READ

Read pages 8 to 11

Purpose: To find out why Mantu is sad.

At last the elephants came to water.

Little Mantu was thirsty. He was so happy to see the cool, clear water that he ran to the river.

He was about to jump in, but his mother chased after him and held him tightly by the tail.

Kim, the oldest elephant, always went in first to look for crocodiles.

"The water is safe," Kim cried.

The elephants began to drink and play in the evening light.

Mantu's mother filled up her trunk and drank the clear cool water.

"I want to do that," thought Mantu.

Then the elephants got washed. They filled their trunks with water and sprayed their dusty backs.

"Wow!" thought Mantu. "I want to do that."

5

PAUSE

Pause at page 11

What are the other elephants doing?

How does Mantu feel? Why?

READ

Read pages 12 and 13

Purpose: To find out what Mantu has to learn to do.

PAUSE

Pause at page 13

What did Mantu want to do? What does Mantu's mother suggest?

Find the words that describe how Mantu felt.
(*sad and a little angry*)

Can you think of skills you needed to practise in order to do them well (e.g. *writing, talking, walking, skipping*).

Please turn to page 15 for Revisit and Respond activities.

But Mantu couldn't use his trunk yet. He was still too young. He could fill his trunk with water, but it fell out before he could drink it.

He had to put his head under the water to drink. He wished he could use his trunk like a **big** elephant.

10

11

Mantu's mother sprayed his back. Mantu tried to spray his mother but he couldn't. The water all fell out of his trunk back into the river.

Little Mantu was sad and a little angry. He wanted to learn how to spray with his trunk.

"You have to practise," said his mother.

"I will!" cried Mantu.

12

13

Lesson 2 (Chapter 2)

RECAP

Recap lesson 1

What happened to Mantu in the first chapter?

What do you think will happen in Chapter 2?

Can you find any clues in Chapter 1 about what might happen in Chapter 2?

READ

Read pages 14 to 17

Purpose: To find out what happened and what it tells us about Mantu's character and Kim's wisdom.

PAUSE

Pause at page 17

What was Mantu doing? What sort of character is Mantu? (*determined – he is practising spraying water; very young – unaware of possible dangers*)

Who was watching over Mantu? What did Kim do? Why? What happened next? Why doesn't Mantu notice the crocodile?

Look at the illustration on pages 16 and 17. What do the expressions on the characters' faces tell you about what they are thinking and feeling?

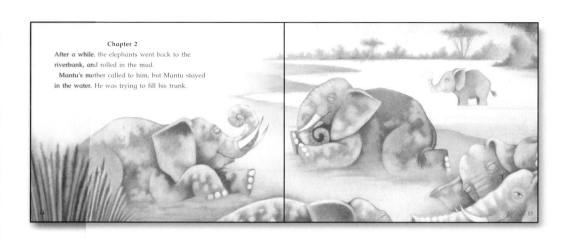

Chapter 2

After a while, the elephants went back to the riverbank, and rolled in the mud.

Mantu's mother called to him, but Mantu stayed in the water. He was trying to fill his trunk.

Suddenly, Kim ROARED. The other elephants looked up to see what was wrong. A crocodile had slipped into the river and was swimming toward Mantu. **Mantu was in terrible danger!**

Mantu didn't see the crocodile, and he didn't hear Kim roaring. He was learning how to use his trunk.

READ

Read pages 18 and 19

Purpose: To notice and discuss how these two pages
are written.

PAUSE

Pause at page 19

What grammar and punctuation does the author use to
show fear/tension/excitement? (*use of commas, short
sentences, capitalization*)

What does Mantu's mother do? Discuss how Mantu's
mother will not leave him.

The crocodile was getting closer and closer to Mantu. Kim **ROARED** again, as loud as she could, and Mantu looked up. He saw the crocodile swimming towards him. He tried to get to the bank, but his feet were stuck in the mud. He cried with fear.

Mantu's mother ran to him. She held onto his tail, and pulled as hard as she could. But Mantu's legs were still stuck in the mud.

Mantu was very, very scared. He knew that crocodiles attack baby elephants.

Read to pages 20 and 21

Purpose: To notice and be ready to comment on the use of illustrations and on the development of Kim's character.

Pause at page 21

What does Kim do to save Mantu? Why is he a good leader of the elephants?

Do you think that the crocodile is afraid?

What words can you think of to describe Kim? (*brave, strong, fierce,* etc)

Ask the children to pick out examples of commas, short sentences, capitalization.

Read pages 22 to the end

Purpose: To find out how Mantu and the other elephants feel.

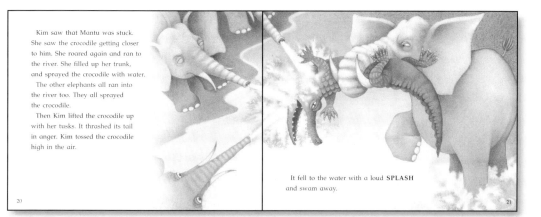

Kim saw that Mantu was stuck.
She saw the crocodile getting closer
to him. She roared again and ran to
the river. She filled up her trunk,
and sprayed the crocodile with water.
    The other elephants all ran into
the river too. They all sprayed
the crocodile.
    Then Kim lifted the crocodile up
with her tusks. It thrashed its tail
in anger. Kim tossed the crocodile
high in the air.

It fell to the water with a loud **SPLASH**
and swam away.

20

21

The other elephants pushed and pulled little
Mantu. Finally, with one sharp tug, they
got him out of the mud.
    Mantu stood on the bank, trembling.
His mother began to stroke him, but
he was still shaking.
    Mantu still had some water in his
trunk. Suddenly, he sprayed the water
all over his mother. Mantu was
amazed when the water flew out
of his trunk!
    "Well done, Mantu," said his mother.

22

23

13

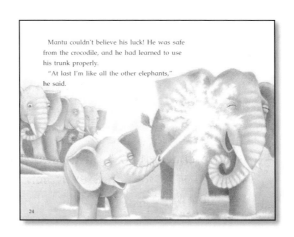

Mantu couldn't believe his luck! He was safe
from the crocodile, and he had learned to use
his trunk properly.
"At last I'm like all the other elephants,"
he said.

24

PAUSE

Pause at page 24

What do the expressions on the faces of the elephants
tell you about how they feel? (*relieved*)

Why was Mantu trembling?

What happened which surprised Mantu?

Which word on page 23 means the same as 'surprised'?
(*amazed*)

What do you think about the ending?

After Reading

Revisit and Respond

Lesson 1

T Ask the children to discuss what they think of Mantu. Go back over the text to locate references to him and make conclusions about his character.

T Ask the children to look through the text gathering all the words and phrases which describe the setting (e.g. *wide open sky; hot, dusty land*). Discuss ideas for other stories using the same setting (e.g. *safari adventures, getting lost in Africa,* etc.).

Lesson 2

T Discuss in detail the character of Kim – using references in the text to her wisdom and age.

T Talk about how the author makes some passages exciting.

T Ask the children to write down the things that Mantu might learn from the story (e.g. *to be patient, to take more care, to listen to his elders* etc.)

T Ask the children in groups to role-play the text.

S Ask the children to list the ways the author makes the text tense and exciting, e.g. *short sentences, capitalization, commas, bold lettering, descriptive adjectives*. Ask them to find examples of each.

Follow-up

Independent Group Activity Work

This book is accompanied by two photocopy masters, one with a reading focus, and one with a writing focus, which support the main teaching objectives of this book. The photocopy masters can be found in the Planning and Assessment Guide.

PCM 43 (*reading*)

PCM 44 (*writing*)

Writing

Guided Writing: Write an exciting paragraph using short sentences, commas, exciting vocabulary and capitalization. You could retell the fight between Kim and the crocodile or make up another incident.

Extended Writing: Write about a time when someone saved you – use all the ideas that we've learned about how to write an exciting story (*short sentences, commas, vocabulary, capitalization*).

Assessment Points

Assess that the children have learnt the main teaching points of the book by checking that they can:

- describe the setting of the book
- describe and discuss the character of Mantu/Kim and how it was developed through actions
- read and identify ways of building up tension in a story.